THE RED BADGE OF COURAGE

Stephen Crane

Academic Industries, Inc.
West Haven, Connecticut 06516

ISBN 0-88301-707-5

Published by
Academic Industries, Inc.
The Academic Building
Saw Mill Road
West Haven, Connecticut 06516

Printed in the United States of America

ABOUT THE AUTHOR

Stephen Crane, born in 1871 in Newark, New Jersey, was the youngest of fourteen children. His father was a Methodist minister, and some critics have suggested that his father's influence contributed to several religious themes in his books.

Crane's most famous book, *The Red Badge of Courage*, was written from accounts of the Civil War, talking to veterans, and reflecting on his own youth. Stephen, like Henry Fleming, was searching for his own identity. He, too, had to pass from a romantic to a realistic view of war.

Stephen Crane

THE RED BADGE OF COURAGE

Mother

Jim Conklin

Henry Fleming

Wilson

General

Less than a hundred years after the United States became a new country, there was a terrible war, bloody and horrible. Henry Fleming, a farm boy in New York State, dreamed of how he would join the army and become a great hero. This is the story of what happened to Henry's dreams.

Ma! Look at what's going on out there. . .and me stuck on the farm! I should be fighting for my country!

You're needed here, Henry. You're all I have to help. And what would happen to the country if all the men-folk went running off to war?

Now you forget about fightin' and bring the cows in.

Yes, Ma.

A few nights later. . . .

What's that? The church bell?

CLANG! CLONG! CLANG! CLANG!

Henry wondered: Was that all Ma was going to say? But when he was ready to leave for camp. . . .

You watch out, Henry, and take care of yourself in this here fightin' business. Don't go thinking you can lick the whole rebel army at the start.

Do your duty, child. If there comes a time when you have to be killed or do a mean thing, why Henry, don't think of anything except what's right. The Lord will take care of us all.

Don't forget the socks I knit you, and your shirts. I've put a cup of blackberry jam with your bundle because I know you like it above all things. Good-bye, Henry. Watch out, and be a good boy.

Good-bye, Ma.

The only enemy soldiers Henry saw were Rebel guards on the other side of the river. One night they talked.

Hey, Reb! You don't look like a bad sort! Why are you fightin' us?

Yank, you are a right good fellow. All the same I might have to take a shot at you one of these days.

Then after weeks of waiting. . . .

I tell you, we'll be fighting tomorrow!

I'll believe it when I see it, Conklin!

Is there going to be a big battle, Jim?

Of course, one of the biggest! The cavalry left this morning, going to Richmond, while we fight here!

A terrible fear, a fear that had been growing in Henry for days took hold of him.
How will I act in battle? What if I run? What if I turn out to be a coward?

Jim! Think any of the boys will run?

Oh, a few maybe. But most will fight like anything after they get started.

Er. . .think you might run yourself, Jim?

Well, if a whole lot of the boys started to run, why, I suppose I'd run, too. But if everybody was standing and fighting, why I'd stand and fight. By, gosh, I would.

There was no battle the next day. But a few days after that. . . .

Didn't I tell you? You'll get your bellyful of fightin' today!

Fall in! On the double!

Like a snake crawling from the darkness of night, the long line of men moved across the countryside.

As they marched the men became happy.

Oh, we'll hang Jeff Davis from an old apple tree, we'll hang Jeff Davis from an old apple tree....

How can they laugh and sing just before a battle? Aren't they afraid?

And when they camped for the night....

You're looking very pale, Henry. What is wrong with you?

Oh, nothing, Wilson.

Cheer up, my boy! This time we're in for a big battle, and we'll lick them good!

How do you know you won't run when the time comes?

Run? Not me! I'll never run! You can bet on that!

Wish I could be so sure.

For days they marched.

How long is this going on? All we got is sore feet and not enough food.

Then, one morning. . . .

Wake up, Henry! We're moving out . . . fast!

It may be my first and last battle, old boy.

Something tells me I'm a goner the first time and. . .I want you to take these letters. . .to. . . my folks.

Whatever you say, Wilson, but. . . .

I don't understand. . .

Suddenly. . . .

Look! Here they come!

Slowly, like a careful workman, Henry loads and fires, loads and fires.

They're falling back!

We've stopped them! We did it!

We showed them, didn't we? We showed them how Yankees can fight!

We sure did!

Whew! But it was hot work, wasn't it?

You bet!

As the Confederates charged again, more than one man dropped his rifle and ran.

They're running! Why should I stay here and be killed?

Stop! Back into line!

No! We'll all be killed!

Running, tripping, sometimes falling, Henry ran blindly, madly.

Got to get away! Got to. . . .

To hide his shame, Henry again runs into the woods, and....

What's that noise?

Nothin' but a darn squirrel.

See? He ran! Even a squirrel runs from danger! It's only natural! I was only doin' a natural thing when I ran...nobody can blame me!

But as he walked through the woods, Henry was frightened by....

Aagh! Dead Man! Dead... Long time.

While the eyes of the dead man stared straight at him, he slowly backed away....

L-looks as though he might stand up an' come after me.

....and ran off again.

It's quiet here. So quiet.

Suddenly, from a distance, came a terrible noise.

The battle! It's started again, worse than ever!

Henry wanted to watch the great battle. But he couldn't face the men of his regiment, so he wandered around and around.

More dead men.

But Henry felt strange being with the wounded.

Darn me if I ever see fellows fight so. Pretty good fight, wasn't it?

Yes.

Where did you get hit, old boy?

That? I... I...that is...why I....

Hey! Where you goin'? What the...I only asked....

Feeling as if everyone knew he had run away, Henry looked sadly at the wounded.

Nobody can call them cowards! Wish I had a wound, too...a red badge of courage!

Suddenly, he saw someone he knew with the wounded.

Ohhh! No....

God! It's Jim...Jim Conklin!

Hello, Henry. Where you been? I thought you got hit.

Glad to see you. There's been so much trouble today. Lord, what a circus! And by gosh, I got shot. Yes, I did.

Let me help you, Jim.

Oh, Jim... oh, Jim....

I'll tell you what I'm afraid of, Henry. . .afraid I'll fall down. . .and them wagons . . .they'll run me over.

I'll take care of you, Jim.

It ain't much to ask, is it? Just pull me out of the road. I'd do it for you, wouldn't I, Henry?

I swear I'll take care of you, Jim! I swear it!

No. . .no. . .leave me be. . . leave me be. . . .

But!

Better take him out of the road. There's a group of wagons coming fast as lightning down the road and he'll get run over.

Oh God!

Nothing we can do for him, friend. You look pretty pale yourself. You'd better take care of your hurt. Where did you get it?

Again Henry felt ashamed.

Oh, don't bother me! Goodbye!

Wha. . .?

Why, friend. . . where you going? Now look here. . .it ain't right! Where you going?

Over there!

I wish I was dead! I'm a coward. . .I ran and everybody's goin' to know it!

Coming to the top of a hill, Henry saw a large group of wagons, teams, and men, all moving along filled with fear.

They're retreating. . . every last one of them! So how can they blame me for running?

But a few minutes later, he saw fresh troops coming up the road toward the battle.

More soldiers moving up! The fighting isn't over!

I should be with them. . .leading the fight. . .proving my bravery.

But how can I go back to my regiment? They'd laugh at me for being a coward.

Then, as another wave of retreating troops swept around him. . . .

What's happened? Have we lost? I've got to find out!

. . . .Henry went off in a daze. . . .

Until. . . .

You seem to be in a pretty bad way, boy!

Well, I'm going your way. The whole gang is going your way. I guess I can give you a lift. What's your regiment? We'll find it, one way or another.

And, at last. . . .

Ah, there you are! There's your regiment! And now old boy, good-bye, and good luck to you!

As Henry stumbled toward the fire. . . .

Halt! Halt! Who goes there?

Wilson! You. . .you here? Why, hello, Wilson!

Well, well! By gosh, I'm glad to see you, Henry!

I gave you up for a goner. I thought you was dead sure enough. What happened to you?

I can't tell him the truth! Got to think of something.

Got separated from the regiment. Terrible fighting over on the right. Had an awful time. Got shot. . .in the head.

What? Why didn't you say so? Poor old boy. . . Wait! Here comes Corporal Simpson!

Who you talking to, Wilson? You're the darndest guard. . .why it's Henry! I thought you was dead!

He got shot in the head, and he's in a fix.

Let's have a look. Hmm. . .You have been grazed by a ball. You've got a strange bump, like you'd been hit with a club. Wilson, you take care of him. I'll go find someone to take your guard duty.

And Wilson did take care of Henry. After bandaging his head. . . .

There's coffee in his canteen. Drink up boy. . .it'll do you good.

Drink it all! Then get into these blankets and have a good night's rest.

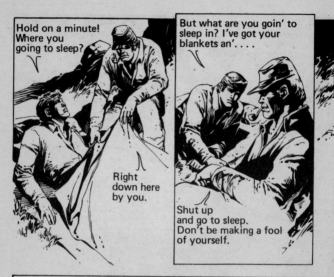

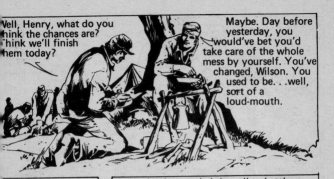

Well, Henry, what do you think the chances are? Think we'll finish them today?

Maybe. Day before yesterday, you would've bet you'd take care of the whole mess by yourself. You've changed, Wilson. You used to be. . .well, sort of a loud-mouth.

Sorry, Wilson. . .I shouldn't have said that.

No, you're right. I have changed. I was a pretty big fool in those days. But being in battle kind of changes a man.

As the bugle sounded the call to battle, Henry took his place in the ranks, sure that this time he would not run.

Well, old boy, here we go again.

We'll show 'em!

Forward. . . march!

Bet he's sorry he gave me those letters yesterday. I'll spring them on him if he start asking about what happened to me during the battle.

Uh. . .Henry. . . those letters I gave you, I guess you may as well give them back.

Oh, sure, Wilson! The poor devil. It makes him feel tough! He's a good fellow. . .I won't make fun of him.

Henry was feeling more sure of himself all the time and thought about the future, when he would be home again, a hero telling of his great adventure.

But when they reached the battleground. . . .

They're moving us around again. . .one place to another. We must be losing.

Gosh, we're ordered around by a bunch of jerks.

Maybe it isn't all the general's fault.

If we fight like the devil and don't whip them, it must be the general's fault.

Maybe you think you fought the whole battle yesterday, Fleming.

Afraid that his running away had been discovered. . . .

Why, no. No. I don't think I fought the whole battle yesterday.

Does he know I ran?

48

I thought I saw a stream back there. Let's get some water.

Sure!

Get some for me, too!

They found no water, but. . . .

Wait! Listen! It's the general!

The enemy's forming for another charge. I fear they'll get through unless we work like thunder to stop them. What troops can you spare?

Get them ready, then. I'll send word to start in about five minutes. It'll be a lot of trouble stopping the Rebs. I don't believe many of your men will get back.

They rushed back to the line with their news.

We're goin' to charge!

We heard the general say so!

Charge, eh? Well, this is real fighting!

And minutes later, when they went into action.

He said not many of us would get back.

As the noise of the battle rose around them, the men stopped at the edge of an open field.

Come on, you fools! You can't stay here. Come on!

Come on, you jerk! Across the lot! We'll all get killed if we stay here!

With a roar of anger, Henry charged.

The flag sergeant. . .he's hit! He's dropping the flag!

Let me have it!

No, Wilson. . . I've got it!

The men fought bravely, but as more Rebel troops were hurled at them, they began to drop back.

Shoot into them! Shoot into them! Blast their souls!

Where you going? Stand and fight!

Fight you devils, or I'll run myself!

The regiment seemed suddenly to come to life, and in a tough hand-to-hand battle, they pushed back the Confederates.

We got them! They're falling back!

For a little while, the battle died down, and the men rested, feeling good with themselves.

Well, old boy, we showed them!

We sure did!

By thunder, Colonel, what an awful mess you made! If your men had only gone a hundred feet further, you would have made a great charge! But as it is. . . .

Well, general, we went as far as we could.

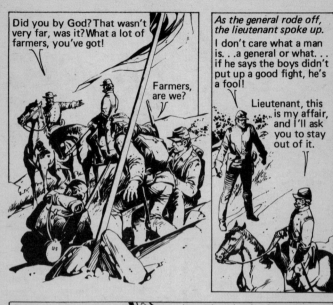

Did you by God? That wasn't very far, was it? What a lot of farmers, you've got!

Farmers, are we?

As the general rode off, the lieutenant spoke up.

I don't care what a man is. . .a general or what. . . if he says the boys didn't put up a good fight, he's a fool!

Lieutenant, this is my affair, and I'll ask you to stay out of it.

Henry and Wilson, like the rest of the men, were angry and upset. . . .

Good thunder! What does he mean calling us farmers?

I wonder what he does want; he must think we went there and played marbles. I never seen such a man. He's crazy!

He's a jerk, that's what!

Then several soldiers came running up with news.

Oh, Fleming, you should have heard!

Heard what?

The colonel said to the lieutenant. . . they were right by us . . .he said, "Who was that boy that carried the flag?"

"That's Fleming," says the lieutenant, "and he's a good soldier. So's Wilson. The two of them led the charge.

He never said it.

He did! And the colonel said, "They deserve to be major generals!"

Guess we didn't do so bad after all!

No matter what the general said!

Now filled with pride, Henry watched as the other regiments took up the battle.

Then it was his turn again!

Let's go men! We're needed out there!

The Confederates came charging in a terrible attack.

The Union soldiers fought back, but the Rebs were protected by a stone wall fence.

We must charge them, or they'll cut us to bits from behind the fence! Charge them!

After them men! Drive them away from the stone wall fence!

The two troops crashed together, and the Union men went over the fence like a giant wave of blue.

Come on! There goes the bugle!

Yep, we're being relieved. Well it's all over.

By God, it is. It is.

Marching away from the battlefield, Henry did a lot of thinking. He still felt some shame because he had run away the previous day. But now he felt proud, too. He had learned a great deal. He had seen death and now had the courage to face it. He was a man. He had earned the right to wear the Red Badge of Courage.

THE END

COMPLETE LIST OF POCKET CLASSICS AVAILABLE

CLASSICS

C 1 Black Beauty
C 2 The Call of the Wild
C 3 Dr. Jekyll and Mr. Hyde
C 4 Dracula
C 5 Frankenstein
C 6 Huckleberry Finn
C 7 Moby Dick
C 8 The Red Badge of Courage
C 9 The Time Machine
C10 Tom Sawyer
C11 Treasure Island
C12 20,000 Leagues Under the Sea
C13 The Great Adventures of Sherlock Holmes
C14 Gulliver's Travels
C15 The Hunchback of Notre Dame
C16 The Invisible Man
C17 Journey to the Center of the Earth
C18 Kidnapped
C19 The Mysterious Island
C20 The Scarlet Letter
C21 The Story of My Life
C22 A Tale of Two Cities
C23 The Three Musketeers
C24 The War of the Worlds
C25 Around the World in Eighty Days
C26 Captains Courageous
C27 A Connecticut Yankee in King Arthur's Court
C28 The Hound of the Baskervilles
C29 The House of the Seven Gables
C30 Jane Eyre
C31 The Last of the Mohicans
C32 The Best of O. Henry
C33 The Best of Poe
C34 Two Years Before the Mast
C35 White Fang
C36 Wuthering Heights
C37 Ben Hur
C38 A Christmas Carol
C39 The Food of the Gods
C40 Ivanhoe
C41 The Man in the Iron Mask
C42 The Prince and the Pauper
C43 The Prisoner of Zenda
C44 The Return of the Native
C45 Robinson Crusoe
C46 The Scarlet Pimpernel

COMPLETE LIST OF POCKET CLASSICS AVAILABLE
(cont'd)

C47 The Sea Wolf
C48 The Swiss Family Robinson
C49 Billy Budd
C50 Crime and Punishment
C51 Don Quixote
C52 Great Expectations
C53 Heidi
C54 The Illiad
C55 Lord Jim
C56 The Mutiny on Board H.M.S. Bounty
C57 The Odyssey
C58 Oliver Twist
C59 Pride and Prejudice
C60 The Turn of the Screw

SHAKESPEARE

S 1 As You Like It
S 2 Hamlet
S 3 Julius Caesar
S 4 King Lear
S 5 Macbeth
S 6 The Merchant of Venice
S 7 A Midsummer Night's Dream
S 8 Othello
S 9 Romeo and Juliet
S10 The Taming of the Shrew
S11 The Tempest
S12 Twelfth Night